Little Voices Christmas

NOVELLO PUBLISHING LIMITED
part of The Music Sales Group
London / New York / Paris / Sydney / Copenhagen / Berlin / Madrid / Tokyo

Published by
Novello Publishing Limited
14-15 Berners Street, London, W1T 3LJ, UK.

Exclusive distributors:
Music Sales Limited
Distribution Centre, Newmarket Road,
Bury St Edmunds, Suffolk, IP33 3YB, UK.

Music Sales Pty Limited
20 Resolution Drive, Caringbah,
NSW 2229, Australia.

Order No. NOV940709
ISBN 978-1-84772-203-4
This book © Copyright 2007 Novello & Company Limited.

Arranged by Barrie Carson Turner.
Edited by Rachel Payne.
Music processed by Paul Ewers Music Design.

Printed in the EU.

www.musicsales.com

All I Want For Christmas Is You

Words & Music by
Mariah Carey & Walter Afanasieff

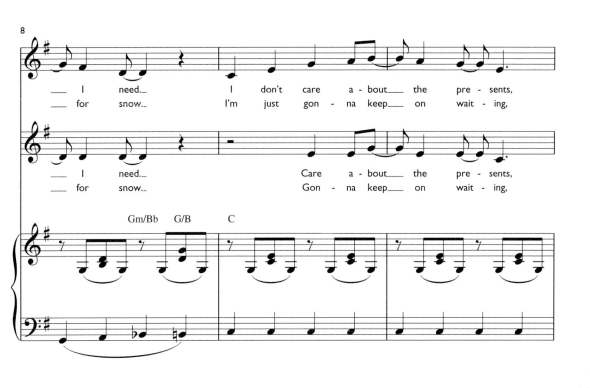

___ my stock - ing there up - on the fi - re - place.__
___ and send_ it to the North Pole for__ Saint Nick.__
___ for Christ - mas this is all I'm ask - ing for.__

___ my stock - ing on the fi - re - place.__
___ and send_ it North Pole for__ Saint Nick.__
___ for Christ - mas all I'm ask - ing for.__

Gm/Bb   G/B

San - ta Claus won't make__ me hap - py with a toy on Christ -
I won't ev - en stay__ a - wake_ to hear those ma - gic rein -
I just want to see__ my ba - by stand - ing right out - side__

San - ta Claus won't make__ me hap - py toy on Christ -
I won't ev - en stay__ a - wake_ to ma - gic rein -
I just want to see__ my ba - by right out - side__

C   Cm/Eb

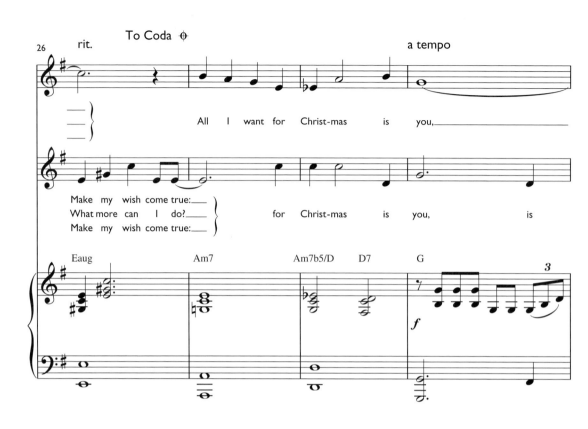

All the lights_ are shin-ing so bright-ly ev-'ry-where,_____

All the lights_ are shin-ing so bright-ly ev-'ry-where,

and the sound_ of child-ren's laugh-ter fills the air._____

and the sound_ of child-ren's laugh-ter fills the air._____

please bring my ba - by to me?

please bring my ba - by to me?

D7

Coda

Slowly (ad lib.)

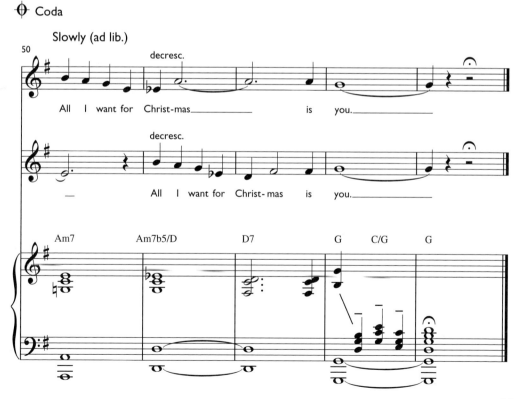

decresc.

All I want for Christ-mas is you.

decresc.

All I want for Christ-mas is you.

Am7 Am7b5/D D7 G C/G G

Little Saint Nick

Words & Music by
Brian Wilson & Michael Love

up in red___ and he spends the whole_ year work-ing out on his sled.___
ski for a wheel and when San - ta hits the gas, man, just watch her___ peel.___ It's the
snow just flies___ and he's cruis-ing ev-'ry pad with a lit - tle sur - prise.___

up in red,___ spends the whole year out on his sled.___
ski for a wheel, San - ta hits the gas, watch her___ peel.___
snow just flies,___ cruis-ing ev - 'ry pad lit - tle sur - prise.___

Dm7   G   Gaug/B   C   C#dim

To Coda

1.

lit - tle Saint Nick.   It's the lit - tle Saint Nick.   2. Just a -

Lit - tle Saint Nick,   lit - tle Saint Nick.

F   G7   C   D7sus   G7

A - run, run rein - deer._____ A -

Saint Nick. A - run, run rein - deer, a - run, run, run.__

G7   F

-run, run rein - deer, aah._____ A - run, run rein - deer._____

Run, run rein - deer, ahh._____ A - run, run rein - deer, a-

Bb   Cm C#dim Bb/D F

A - run, run rein - deer. 3. And a -

run, run, run.___ He don't miss no one.

D   D7/A   G7

Coda

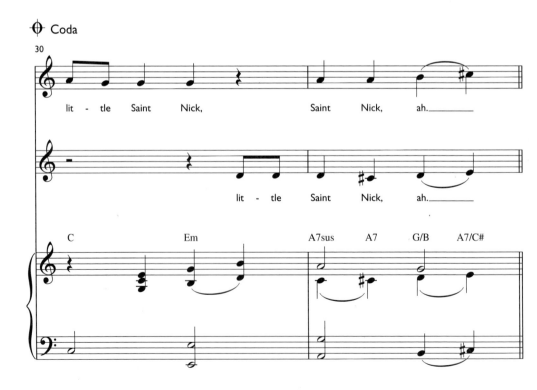

lit - tle Saint Nick, Saint Nick, ah._____

lit - tle Saint Nick, ah._____

C   Em   A7sus   A7   G/B   A7/C#

Ooh, ah, mer-ry Christ-mas Saint Nick, this time of year._

Ooh._____ Christ-mas comes this time each year._

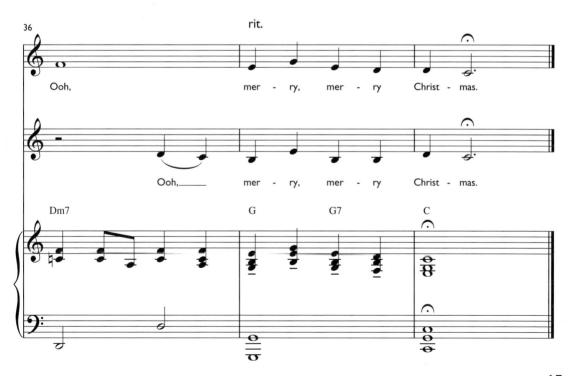

Ooh, mer - ry, mer - ry Christ - mas.

Ooh,_____ mer - ry, mer - ry Christ - mas.

Silent Night

Words by Joseph Mohr
Music by Franz Gruber

Louder

20

With the dawn of re - deem - ing grace, Je - sus, Lord at thy

With the dawn of re - deem - ing grace, Je - sus, Lord at thy

birth,_____ Je - sus, Lord at thy birth._____

birth, Je - sus, Lord at thy birth._____

I Saw Mommy Kissing Santa Claus

Words & Music by Tommie Connor

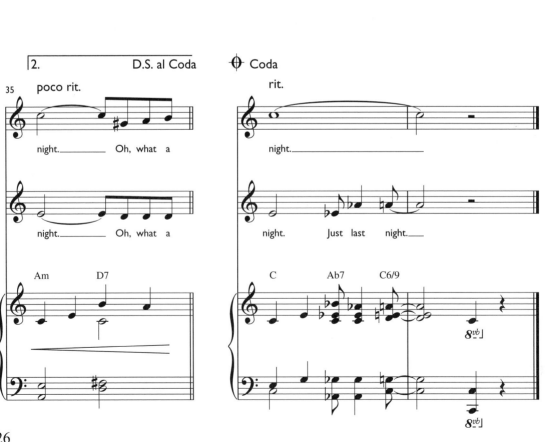

We Wish You A Merry Christmas

Traditional

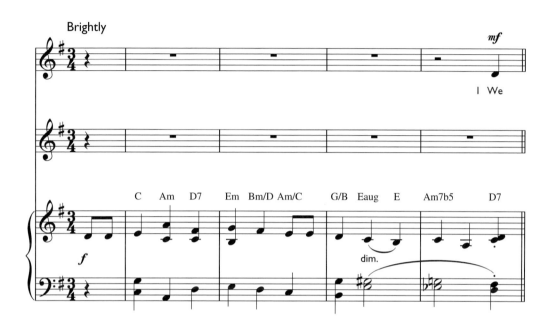

wish you a mer-ry Christ-mas, And a hap-py New Year. Good tid-ings we
all want some fig-gy pud-ding, So bring some right here.

Christ-mas, And a hap-py New Year. Good
pud-ding, So bring some right here.

B+ B B7 Em G/D C D7 G

bring to you and your kin; We wish you a mer-ry Christ-mas, And a

tid - ing we bring to you and your kin____ at Christ-mas, And a

Bm Em7 A7 D D7 G D/F# Em G/D D/C G/B

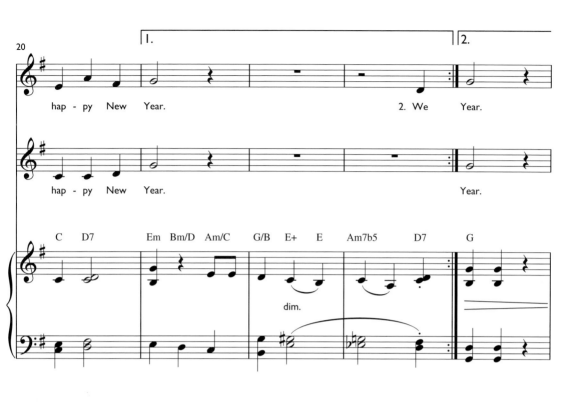

won't go un-til we get some, So bring some right here. Good tid - ings we

won't go un-til we get some, So bring some here! Good

Baug   B   Em   G/D Am7/C D7   G   Em

cresc.

bring   To   you and your   kin;   We wish you a mer-ry Christ-mas And a

tid - ings   we   bring to your   kin;   We wish you a mer-ry Christ-mas And a

Bm   Em7 A7   Bb D7/A   G   D/F#   Em   G/D D/C G/B

Track Listing

1. All I Want For Christmas Is You
(Carey/Afanasieff) Sony/ATV Music Publishing (UK) Limited/
Universal/MCA Music Limited
Full Performance

2. Little Saint Nick
(Wilson/Love) Rondor Music (London) Limited
Full Performance

3. Silent Night
(Mohr/Gruber) Dorsey Brothers Music Limited
Full Performance

4. I Saw Mommy Kissing Santa Claus
(Connor) Blue Ribbon Music Limited
Full Performance

5. We Wish You A Merry Christmas
(Traditional) Dorsey Brothers Music Limited
Full Performance

6. All I Want For Christmas Is You
(Carey/Afanasieff) Sony/ATV Music Publishing (UK) Limited/
Universal/MCA Music Limited
Piano Accompaniment

7. Little Saint Nick
(Wilson/Love) Rondor Music (London) Limited
Piano Accompaniment

8. Silent Night
(Mohr/Gruber) Dorsey Brothers Music Limited
Piano Accompaniment

9. I Saw Mommy Kissing Santa Claus
(Connor) Blue Ribbon Music Limited
Piano Accompaniment

10. We Wish You A Merry Christmas
(Traditional) Dorsey Brothers Music Limited
Piano Accompaniment